Introduction to Public Speaking

COMM1110

2021–2022

Department of Communication Studies
University of Georgia

XanEdu

Printed in the United States of America

ISBN 13: 978-1-71149-436-4

Acknowledgment:

Cover photo © University of Georgia. Photographer: Andrew Davis Tucker.

This workbook is the product of the work of multiple generations of faculty and graduate students in the Department of Communication Studies. This edition was compiled and edited by Bjørn Stillion Southard, Savannah Downing, and Carly Fabian.

4750 Venture Drive, Suite 400
Ann Arbor, MI 48108
800-562-2147
www.xanedu.com

TABLE OF CONTENTS

Course Information, Policies, and Resources _____

   Academic Honesty _____ 3

   Research Requirement Process_____ 5

   Extra Credit: Attending a COMM Speech Event _____ 9

   Criteria Used for Evaluating Speeches _____ 13

   Using PowerPoint in a Public Speech _____ 12

   Using Tables Well _____ 14

   Types of Supporting Material: S.U.P.P.O.R.T.S._____ 17

*Activities*_____

   1--Constructing a Theme _____ 19

   2--Audience Analysis _____ 21

   3--Adapting to Your Audience_____ 23

   4--Speech Topic Audience Analysis _____ 25

   5-- Evidence Research _____ 29

   6--Testing Evidence _____ 31

   7--Researching Speech Topics _____ 33

   8--Supporting Material _____ 35

   9--Using Paradigms to Strengthen Arguments _____ 37

   10--Flawed Introductions _____ 39

   11-- Introduction Draft Evaluation _____ 41

   12--Main Points _____ 43

   13--Full-Sentence Outline Peer Critique _____ 45

   14--Working Outline _____ 49

   15--Language and Style _____ 55

   16—Parsimony _____ 57

   17--Free Speech, Decorum, and Ceremonial Speaking _____ 59

   18--"Toasting Public Speaking" Speech Activity _____ 61

   19--Components of Speaking Activity_____ 63

   20--Constructing a Counterargument _____ 65

   21--Policy Introduction Draft_____ 67

   22--Delivering Verbal Citations _____ 69

   23--Vocal Variety _____ 71

Sample Outline and Evaluation Forms _____

Sample Full-Sentence Outline _____ 73

Personal Report of Public Speaking Anxiety _____ 77

Peer- Evaluations: Holistic _____ 79

Peer-Evaluations: Delivery _____ 87

Peer-Evaluations: Supporting Materials _____ 89

Peer-Evaluations: Language _____ 91

Academic Honesty

All students are responsible for knowing the University's policy on academic honesty. All academic work submitted in this course must be your own unless you have received my permission to collaborate and have properly acknowledged receiving assistance. It is my responsibility to uphold the University's honesty policy and report my belief of dishonesty to the Office of the Vice President for Instruction.

You read the above words multiple times each semester. You signed the UGA Honor Code before you were even admitted to UGA. Yet, somehow, students still end up violating the academic honesty policy each semester. In order to avoid becoming one of those students, review *A Culture of Honesty* (http://uga.edu/honesty) and the following examples. The examples below are designed to help you better understand how academic honesty pertains to your public speaking class. **Please note**: the following is not a complete list of all academic honesty offenses.

Students who have **violated** the honesty code in public speaking courses have:

- had friends/classmates sign in for them when they were absent
- signed in for classmates when they were absent
- presented a speech that was prepared by someone other than the speaker
- passed off someone else's language as their own (i.e., they failed to let the audience know that they were providing a direct quotation)
- presented a speech that they had prepared for a different course and received credit for
- plagiarized any portion of their speech—even just a sentence
- copied one section of a previous speech into another speech (i.e., using a section from your informative speech in your policy speech without changing it)
- given false excuses for missing a speech or class
- studied from old exams that the instructor did not provide (they received the exams from friends)
- used their books/materials to complete closed book assignments
- gone to the restroom during an exam to review notes
- used a sample speech as a template and tinkered with the wording to fit their topic

> **Want to be sure you are not violating the honor code?**
> Talk to your instructor or contact the Academic Honesty Coordinator at (706) 542.4336 or by e-mail at: honesty@uga.edu

If your instructor suspects that you have violated the honor code, the following steps will be taken:

1. Your instructor will complete a Report of Possible Academic Dishonesty form and submit it to the Office of the Vice President for Instruction.

2. You will be notified by the Office of the Vice President for Instruction. **Please note**: you should not discuss this matter with your instructor until the Facilitated Discussion.
3. A Facilitated Discussion between you, your instructor, and a third party will be scheduled.
4. At the Facilitated Discussion, the possible offense will be discussed and hopefully resolved. If you are found guilty of violating the honor code, a consequence will be determined.
5. If the issue is not resolved during the Facilitated Discussion, a Continued Discussion with an Academic Honesty Panel will be held.

In order to avoid violating the honor code, some students do not utilize helpful activities or resources. Examples of behavior that does not violate the academic honesty policy:

- Reviewing course material and studying for exams with classmates
- Incorporating advice about your own speech from your instructor and classmates into your speech without verbally citing them
- Using previous exams/quizzes provided by the instructor to study for upcoming exams/quizzes
- Reviewing sample speeches provided by the instructor to help you construct your own speech

RESEARCH REQUIREMENT PROCESS

The Communication Studies Department requires all students taking COMM1110 and COMM1500 to satisfy a departmental research requirement. Students must earn research credit for each Communication Studies class that requires or offers research participation (e.g., students cannot use one research opportunity to apply to two classes). Students must earn 2 research credits per class to complete the research requirement.

The Research Requirement must be completed on or before Friday of Week 14 (i.e., the Friday before Reading Day). Failure to fulfill the research requirement by the due date will result in a grade of Incomplete (I). In order to remove the Incomplete (I), you must complete the research requirement in a future semester on SONA, noting the instructor is "from a previous semester," and then email that instructor.

Three research options are offered to fulfill this requirement. Students may complete any combination of the options to earn the 2 credits required.
- Option 1: Participation in a lab-based research study (2 credits)
- Option 2: Participation in an online study (1 credit)
- Option 3: Summarize a Communication research article (1 credit)

HOW TO ACCESS AVAILABLE RESEARCH OPPORTUNITIES:

Research opportunities will be posted regularly during the semester at: https://uga-comm.sona-systems.com. Once you are at this website, you need to (1) log into the system to view the list of available studies, (2) sign up for studies you are interested in and qualify for, and (3) track your progress throughout the semester. The system will also track when you receive credit for a study.

For new users: If you are a first-time user to the system, click the "***MyID login***" to authenticate your identity using your UGA MyID. On the next page, you will be able to request an account. You will be required to provide some basic information about yourself and your course information. After submitting the form, you will receive an email notification immediately.

A detailed instruction manual is available here: https://comm.uga.edu/research-opportunities
You can also watch video tutorial here: https://www.youtube.com/watch?v=_1OnT2ZU6QQ

Important: when signing up for a research opportunity, you *must* specify the correct instructor and course name for which the credit(s) should be assigned. If you don't see the instructor/course listed in SONA, contact commrp617@uga.edu.

OPTION 1:
PARTICIPATE IN A LAB-BASED COMMUNICATION RESEARCH STUDY
2 Credits

A **lab-based** research study involves you physically attending a scheduled research lab session in Caldwell Hall or other lab space on campus. The Department of Communication Studies

regards student participation in research studies as an educational experience for the participant, the researcher, and for the department. Student participation is appreciated and essential to the research of the Department of Communication Studies. Research contributions made
by students are a lasting part of the body of social scientific knowledge about communication. The guidelines for research participation are as follows:

STEP 1: SIGN-UP FOR A <u>LAB-BASED</u> RESEARCH STUDY.

1. Check the Communication Research Participation website regularly during the semester to look for studies: https://uga-comm.sona-systems.com
2. When a study becomes available:
   a. Make sure that you qualify to participate in the study (e.g., ensure that you meet all parameters set by the researcher or by the study).
   b. Make sure it is **lab-based:** A lab-based research study involves you physically attending a scheduled research lab session in Caldwell Hall or other lab space on campus. Online research studies (i.e., completing an online survey from home) are described below.
3. Sign-up (register for the study). Be sure to note what timeslot (session) you chose to participate, what will be expected of you, the approximate amount of time the study will take to complete, and the researcher's contact information.
4. After signing up, you must participate in the research study to complete the research requirement.

STEP 2: PARTICIPATE IN THE LAB-BASED RESEARCH STUDY.

1. Researchers may send you a follow-up e-mail to provide more detailed instructions. Make sure you follow the instructions provided in the email. You will also receive an automated email reminder of your study appointment the day before it is scheduled.
2. *Because you are signing up for a study that requires you to physically attend a research lab*:
   a. You must show up at the designated time and location.
   b. When you show up for the study, please sign in using ***<u>both</u>*** your name <u>and</u> your instructor's name. The researchers need this information to ensure you receive participation credit for fulfilling the research requirement.
   c. Note: If you must miss an appointment due to illness or emergency, please email the researcher and let him/her know.
3. The researcher will grant you research credit through the online research participation system. You will receive a notification e-mail when you receive credit(s) for a study. Your instructor can view your credits through the research participation system as well.
4. The researcher will grant you research credits as soon as possible, or within *48 hours of the study closing*, depending on their study needs. This means your credit may not be posted until weeks after you have participated in the study.
5. If for some reason you do not receive credits for participating in a study, check with the researcher.
6. Participation in a study must be completed **on or before Friday of Week 14 (i.e., the Friday before Reading Day.**

OPTION 2:
PARTICIPATE IN AN ONLINE COMMUNICATION RESEARCH STUDY
1 Credit

An **online** study is one that is completed at your own convenience via an emailed link to a research study. As noted above, student participation is appreciated and essential to the research of the Department of Communication Studies. The guidelines for research participation are as follows:

STEP 1: SIGN-UP FOR AN <u>ONLINE</u> RESEARCH STUDY.
    1.   Check the Communication Research Participation website regularly during the semester to look for studies: https://uga-comm.sona-systems.com
    2.   When a study becomes available:
        a.   Make sure that you qualify to participate in the study (e.g., ensure that you meet all parameters set by the researcher or by the study).
    3.   Sign-up (register for the study). Be sure to note when the online survey link will expire, what will be expected of you, the approximate amount of time the study will take to complete, and the researcher's contact information.
    4.   After signing up, you must participate in the online study to complete the research requirement.

STEP 2: PARTICIPATE IN THE ONLINE STUDY.
    1.   Researchers may send you a follow-up e-mail to provide more detailed instructions. Make sure you follow the instructions provided in the email.
    2.   If you sign up for an online study, *it is presumed that you will participate in the study shortly after you sign up for it*.
    3.   The researcher will grant you research credit through the online research participation system. You will receive a notification e-mail when you receive credit(s) for a study. Your instructor can view your credits through the research participation system as well.
    4.   The researcher will grant you research credits as soon as possible, or within *48 hours of the study closing*, depending on their study needs. This means your credit may not be posted until weeks after you have participated in the study.
    5.   If for some reason you do not receive credit for participating in a study, check with the researcher.
    6.   Participation in a study must be completed **on or before Friday of Week 14 (i.e., the Friday before Reading Day.**

OPTION 3:
SUMMARIZE A COMMUNICATION RESEARCH ARTICLE
1 Credit

This option allows students to read current research published in the Communication discipline. The objective is for students to read the article and apply it to their life experiences, thereby demonstrating the ability to understand the relevance of research in lived experience. This option will be available **from the beginning of the 13th week of the semester to the Friday before Reading Day**. Students must sign-up, select an article, and complete the option all through the SONA system. Guidelines for completion of the research article summary are as follows:

STEP 1: SIGN-UP TO SUMMARIZE A RESEARCH ARTICLE
1. Check the Communication Research Participation website beginning the 13th week of the semester to register to complete this option: https://uga-comm.sona-systems.com

STEP 2: SELECT ONE RESEARCH ARTICLE FROM OPTIONS ON SONA
1. Select ONE research article from the two options provided.
2. Read your chosen article at least two times.

STEP 3: COMPLETE QUESTIONS AND SUMMARY OF THE ARTICLE ON SONA
You MUST correctly answer the closed format questions AND submit a short essay applying the study findings to your own life experiences to earn credit for the research requirement. Failure to complete any portion of the below means you cannot pass the research requirement.
1. Answer closed format questions about the research article.
2. Write a short essay applying the findings of the study to your own life experience.

   This short essay should have this structure:
   1. State the generalization from the study you are focusing on
   2. Describe the experience you believe is relevant to the generalization
   3. Explain how it aligns with the study's results or complicates them
   4. Offer any additional thoughts

Your essay should provide at least one unique, personal experience that illustrates or complicates the results of the study. For example, if the study indicates that self-disclosure of taboo information is more likely with strangers who you are not likely to meet again than with casual acquaintances, you might recount an incident when you told a stranger on a plane something that you had told no casual acquaintances. Or, complicating the study results, you might think of an instance when you told a casual acquaintance something you hadn't told anyone else, but explain why you think that this "taboo" subject did not seem forbidding to disclose to this person (or seemed desirable to disclose to this person).

1.   The department will grant you research credit through the online research participation system. You will receive a notification e-mail when you receive credit(s) for a study. Your instructor can view your credits through the research participation system as well.
2.   Completion of the summary of the research article must be done **on or before the Friday before Reading Day.**
3.   If, after the Friday before Reading Day, you have not received credit for completing this assignment, check with the SONA director at commrp617@uga.edu.

*Name:*_____   *Section:*_____

Extra Credit: **Attending a COMM Speech Event**

Directions: Please complete the following prompts for either the COMM Public Speaking Competition or the Georgia Debate Union's Russell Foundation Public Debate. You may only receive credit for one of these events. It is worth ½ of 1% of your final grade. This sheet must be completed and returned to your instructor within one week of the event.

Name of the event: _____

Date and location of the event _____

1. What are general strengths of the speakers? Provide a few specific examples in this paragraph connected to class concepts (use names of speakers).

2. What were areas of distraction or weakness in the speeches? Provide a few specific examples in this paragraph connected to class concepts (use names of speakers).

3. Identify a particular speaker and elaborate what drew you to this speaker (perhaps positively, perhaps negatively).

Criteria Used for Evaluating Speeches

The *average speech* (grade C) should meet the following criteria:

- Conform to the kind of speech assigned—informative, persuasive, etc.
- Be ready for presentation on the assigned date
- Conform to the time limit
- Fulfill any special requirements of the assignment—preparing an outline, using visual aids, conducting an interview, etc.

- Have a clear specific purpose and central idea
- Have an identifiable introduction, body, and conclusion
- Show reasonable directness and competence in delivery
- Be free of serious error in grammar, pronunciation, and word usage

The *above average speech* (grade B) should meet the preceding criteria and also:

- Deal with a challenging topic
- Fulfill all major functions of a speech introduction and conclusion
- Displays clear organization of main points and supporting materials
- Support main points with evidence that meets the tests of accuracy, relevance, objectivity, and sufficiency
- Exhibit proficient use of connectives—transitions, internal previews, internal summaries, and signposts
- Be delivered skillfully enough so as not to distract attention from the speaker's message

The *superior speech* (grade A) should meet the preceding criteria and also:

- Constitute a genuine contribution by the speaker to the knowledge or beliefs of the audience
- Sustain positive interest, feeling, and/or commitment among the audience
- Contain elements of vividness and special interest in the use of language
- Be delivered in a fluent, polished manner that strengthens the impact of the speaker's message

The below average speech (grade D or F) is seriously deficient in the criteria required for the C speech.

Using PowerPoint in a Public Speech

As a student, you've likely sat through many PowerPoint presentations. However, frequent viewing of PowerPoint slides does not necessarily correlate with the ability to create an effective PowerPoint presentation to accompany your speech. The way an instructor uses a PowerPoint presentation to teach a concept is different from the way you will use PowerPoint in your speech. If you are planning to use PowerPoint as a visual aid for your speech, review the principles of visual aids chapter in the book before you begin. Then, consider the following guidelines and tips.

General Guidelines for PowerPoint: PowerPoint can be a smart addition to your presentation if it is used effectively. Keep the following guidelines in mind:

Need help creating your PowerPoint presentation?

You can access free written and video PowerPoint tutorials on Microsoft Office's support page:

http://office.microsoft.com/en-us/support/

OR

Log-on to LinkedIn Learning, which has a variety of tutorials for all experience levels. Go the following site and follow the instructions:

https://eits.uga.edu/learning_and_training/linkedinlearning/

- Use colors, fonts, and slide design to engage, not distract, your audience. Simplicity is key when creating your presentation to accompany a speech.
- Do not create a slide to accompany each of your points. Remember, you should only use a visual aid if you need to make a point more interesting, need help communicating complex information, want to improve the audience's comprehension and retention of an idea, or advance an argument.
- Place blank slides between content slides so your audience will turn their attention back to you after you are done with the slide.
- Give credit where credit is due. Be sure to provide citations information for your sources. See below for more information about citations.
- Test-drive your slideshow on the classroom computer. Many times PowerPoint presentations fail to load in the minutes before a student's speech. Work out the kinks before the day of your speech.
- When practicing your speech, include your PowerPoint presentation each time.

Providing citations: Even though style guides, such as MLA and APA, do not provide specific rules for how to cite sources in a PowerPoint presentation, it is import to cite any research or information that you found from sources. The goal of citation is to let the audience know that you found the information from a source and to provide the audience with citation information should they want to know more or look into your source.

Keep the following in mind when incorporating sources in your PowerPoint:

- Your citation should provide basic information such as author's name, title, source, date, and other important information.
- The citation should be big enough you're your audience to read but should not interfere with the message of the slide.
- You can provide your citation in the footer section of the slide or on a bibliography slide at the end of the presentation.

Common PowerPoint Mistakes: As you are crafting your presentation, work to avoid these common mistakes:

- **Too much content**: Some people put everything they hope to say on their PowerPoint slides. This is no longer a visual aid, but instead your outline. Even though a PowerPoint presentation that is loaded with content might be helpful for you when you are copying down notes during lecture, it is not necessary for a public speech. If you put your entire speech on a visual, your audience will likely read your visual instead of listening to you speak. Remember to keep your PowerPoint *visual*, not verbal.
- **Too little preparation**: It is easy to spot a speaker who has not practiced with their PowerPoint or is not familiar enough with the software. The following are examples of students who were ill-prepared to use PowerPoint:
    o Asking the instructor for help loading the PowerPoint presentation
    o Forgetting to talk about some slides
    o Exiting out of the presentation before the presentation is over
    o Failing to embed video and images correctly

Be sure your practice with your PowerPoint several times before you give your speech. If you are not familiar with how to embed video and images, visit the resources listed on the previous page.

- **Confusing layout**: The design options for your PowerPoint presentation are nearly endless. However, some students choose layouts and designs that make it difficult for audience members to decipher the content. Avoid the following mistakes:
    o Using light colored fonts that do not stand out on the screen.
    o Choosing complex backgrounds that compete with the purpose of the slide
    o Capitalizing all words or formatting font in ways that are off-putting to audience members
- **No blank slides**: Audience members are easily distracted. When you leave a slide up on the screen after you have finished discussing it, audience members will be tempted to continue studying it. You do not want them to do this! You want them to move with you onto your next point. Place a blank slide between all slides to encourage your audience to shift their attention back to you.

Using Tables Well

Tables of data are often helpful to audiences. However, the kind of table that is used in a written communication cannot be effectively shared in an oral communication situation. There are two primary problems that speakers face in sharing tables with audiences. First, audiences may get confused about what to focus on when they are listening to a speaker and looking at a large amount of data. Second, audiences are unlikely to have enough time to process more than three to six pieces of information in a table. There are four rules of thumb that can help deal with these constraints adapt pieces of information from a large table to the oral communication situation:

#1 Table Only the Information You NEED to Talk About

#2 Use Color and Bolding to Emphasize Differences

#3 Build the Table Line by Line as You Talk It Through

#4 Include all Relevant Labels

Here is an Example:

Imagine that you wanted to explain how the risk of heart disease changes by age. You might find the following table from the Centers for Disease Control:

TABLE 1. Age-adjusted prevalence* of coronary heart disease,[†] by selected characteristics --- Behavioral Risk Factor Surveillance System, United States, 2006--2010

Characteristic	2006		2007		2008		2009		2010		p value for linear trend	% change from 2006 to 2010
	%	(95% CI)	%	(95% CI)	%	(95% CI)	%	(95% CI)	%	(95% CI)		
Total	6.7	(6.5-6.9)	6.2	(6.1-6.4)	6.3	(6.2-6.5)	5.8	(5.7-5.9)	6.0	(5.9-6.1)	<0.01	-10.4
Age group (yrs)												
18-44	1.6	(1.4-1.8)	1.5	(1.4-1.7)	1.4	(1.3-1.5)	1.2	(1.1-1.4)	1.2	(1.1-1.4)	<0.01	-25.0
45-64	7.7	(7.4-8.0)	7.2	(6.9-7.4)	7.2	(7.0-7.5)	6.8	(6.6-7.0)	7.1	(6.9-7.3)	<0.01	-7.8
≥65	21.1	(20.5-21.6)	19.8	(19.3-20.2)	20.6	(20.2-21.0)	18.7	(18.3-19.0)	19.8	(19.5-20.2)	<0.01	-6.2
Sex												
Men	8.5	(8.3-8.8)	8.0	(7.8-8.2)	8.2	(8.0-8.4)	7.5	(7.3-7.7)	7.8	(7.6-7.9)	<0.01	-8.2
Women	5.2	(5.0-5.4)	4.8	(4.7-5.0)	4.9	(4.7-5.0)	4.4	(4.2-4.5)	4.6	(4.5-4.7)	<0.01	-11.5
Race/Ethnicity[§]												
Overall												
White	6.4	(6.3-6.6)	6.0	(5.9-6.1)	6.1	(6.0-6.2)	5.6	(5.5-5.7)	5.8	(5.7-5.9)	<0.01	-9.4
Black	6.4	(5.9-6.9)	6.3	(5.8-6.8)	6.3	(5.9-6.7)	5.8	(5.4-6.9)	6.5	(6.1-6.9)	0.68	1.6
Hispanic	6.9	(6.2-7.8)	6.8	(6.2-7.6)	6.9	(6.3-7.6)	5.7	(5.2-6.3)	6.1	(5.6-6.6)	0.01	-11.6
Asian or Native Hawaiian/Other Pacific Islander	5.1	(3.8-6.8)	3.1	(2.4-4.0)	4.8	(3.8-6.0)	4.2	(3.4-5.2)	3.9	(3.3-4.7)	0.47	-23.5
American Indian/Alaska Native	11.3	(9.5-13.5)	12.0	(10.4-13.8)	11.1	(9.7-12.6)	9.8	(8.4-11.5)	11.6	(10.1-13.4)	0.58	2.7

Obviously, if you put that table up on the screen, the audience would have a hard time attending to the information you were interested in.

The information you want to present is only part of the table:

Age group (yrs)												
18-44	1.6	(1.4--1.8)	1.5	(1.4--1.7)	1.4	(1.3--1.5)	1.2	(1.1--1.4)	1.2	(1.1--1.4)	<0.01	-25.0
45-64	7.7	(7.4--8.0)	7.2	(6.9--7.4)	7.2	(7.0--7.5)	6.8	(6.6--7.0)	7.1	(6.9--7.3)	<0.01	-7.8
≥65	21.1	(20.5--21.6)	19.8	(19.3--20.2)	20.6	(20.2--21.0)	18.7	(18.3--19.0)	19.8	(19.5--20.2)	<0.01	-6.2

This, however, is still more information than a general audience will need or want.

So select the key columns, and then build the table line by line as you talk through each line. And use color to highlight focal points. Like this:

Slide 1:

Age	2006 %		2007 %		2008 %		2009 %		2010 %		P for linear trend	% change from 2006 to 2010
18-44	1.6		1.5		1.4		1.2		1.2		<0.01	-25.0

Slide 2:

THEN ADD (AS YOU TALK)

Age	2006 %		2007 %		2008 %		2009 %		2010 %		P for linear trend	% change from 2006 to 2010
18-44	1.6		1.5		1.4		1.2		1.2		<0.01	-25.0
45-46	7.7		7.2		7.2		6.8		7.1		<.0.01	-7.8

By the time you get to slide three, you've presented a lot of data, but it is clear to the audience!

Age	2006 %		2007 %		2008 %		2009 %		2010 %		P for linear trend	% change from 2006 to 2010
18-44	1.6		1.5		1.4		1.2		1.2		<0.01	-25.0
45-64	7.7		7.2		7.2		6.8		7.1		<.0.01	-7.8
>65	21.1		19.8		20.6		18.7		19.8		<0.01	-6.2

ACTIVITY: Now you try. Create three slides using color and careful selecting of data to present some point from the following table from the US Census Bureau:

Table H-3. Mean Household Income Received by Each Fifth and Top 5 Percent, All Races: 1967 to 2013

(Households as of March of the following year. Income in current and 2013 CPI-U-RS adjusted dollars (28))

CURRENT DOLLARS

Year	Lowest fifth	Second fifth	Third fifth	Fourth fifth	Highest fifth	Top 5 percent
2013 (38)	11,651	30,509	52,322	83,519	185,206	322,343
2012	11,490	29,696	51,179	82,098	181,905	318,052
2011	11,239	29,204	49,842	80,080	178,020	311,444
2010 (37)	10,994	28,532	49,167	78,877	169,391	287,201
2009 (36)	11,552	29,257	49,534	78,694	170,844	295,388
2008	11,656	29,517	50,132	79,760	171,057	294,709
2007	11,551	29,442	49,968	79,111	167,971	287,191
2006	11,352	28,777	48,223	76,329	168,170	297,405
2005	10,655	27,357	46,301	72,825	159,583	281,155
2004 (35)	10,244	26,212	44,411	70,026	151,438	263,896
2003	9,996	25,678	43,588	68,994	147,078	253,239
2002	9,990	25,400	42,802	67,326	143,743	251,010
2001	10,136	25,468	42,629	66,839	145,970	260,464
2000 (30)	10,157	25,361	42,233	65,653	142,269	252,400

Types of Supporting Material: S.U.P.P.O.R.T.S.

	Description	Strengths	Weaknesses	Strategies
Stories **a.k.a. Narratives**	Narratives that illustrate a resolution through plot structure	Audience involvement. Shows rather than tells.	Complicated. Long. Unrepresentative.	Only use once. Pair with shorter, representative evidence.
Universals **a.k.a. Bumper Stickers**	Generally held maxims, proverbs, slogans, principles or abstract "truths" usually without author or origin.	Digestible. Flexible. Representative.	Abstract. Reductive.	Use as supplement. Pair with unrepresentative evidence.
Parallels **a.k.a. Analogies**	Makes an unknown vehicle known by transferring a specific tenor from a known vehicle	Translation. Audience involvement. Shows rather than tells.	Reductive (only one tenor). Abstract. Complicated.	Use metaphors when tenor is immediately apparent. Pair with less complicated evidence
Proofs **a.k.a. Rhetorical Arguments**	Evidence that words through style, performance, and linguistic play	Shows rather than tells. (Often) short. Stylistic.	Lack empirical reference. May be appear preachy or old-fashioned.	Keep short. Don't cluster. Pair with empirically verifiable evidence.
Occurrences **a.k.a. Case Studies**	Empirically verifiable examples or incidents	Empirically verifiable. Easy to use	Tell rather than show. Lack audience involvement.	Cluster for stronger impact (extended occurrences).
Rebuttals **a.k.a. Refutations**	Acknowledgement of and response to competing points of view that are commonly held in order to strengthen a position	Enhances credibility. Engages audience. Melds easily with other evidence. Helps the speaker consider weaknesses of position.	Speaker may appear defensive. Require careful audience analysis. May raise doubts that did not exist.	Only rebut objections that are *likely* held. Do not rebut for show. Ground rebuttals: use as form for testimony, occurrences, and statistics.
Testimony **a.k.a. Experts (2 Types: Referent and Authority)**	Explanations, claims, or interpretations from others made legitimate by credentials, experience, or quality of insight	Easy to use. Enhance speaker's credibility. May add more insight to the speech's perspective. Satisfy audience expectations (if not desires).	Complicates delivery. May miss their mark. Often sacrifice perspective for credentials. May be unrepresentative	Consider referential power and authority power. Translate. Quote directly only when eloquently expressed. Look for perspective not just credentials. Include credibility statement.
Statistics **a.k.a. Quantifiable Evidence**	Quantifiable measurements (numbers, percentages, study results, etc.)	Easily show scope or magnitude. Satisfy audience expectations (if not desires). Representative.	Lack emotional connection; fail to commit the audience. Often overused. Hard to deliver.	Always translate or interpret. Never pile up. Incorporate or pair with stores, occurrences, universals and analogies.

S.U.P.P.O.R.T.S. is adapted from the V.A.S.E.S. model presented in Huxman and Campbell, *The Rhetorical Act: Thinking, Speaking, and Writing Critically*, 3rd ed., 2003.

1--Constructing a Theme

Directions: Below you will find a series of facts about two different speakers. For each speaker, come up with a theme that could guide their speech of introduction. Then, organize the data into a speech of introduction for each speaker. You do not need to use each fact in the speech, but you should have 3-5 examples from the list to support your theme.

Casey:

- Grew up on in a small town in southern Georgia

- Only child

- Transferred to UGA this semester from the University of North Carolina

- Chose UGA because of the music program

- Started playing piano at the age of 3

- Plays golf often, but not well

- Twisted ankle at mile 24 of her first and only marathon but finished anyway

- Plays the piano for weddings most weekends

- Has played the piano for the governor

- Has never been outside the US but hopes to travel abroad while at UGA

(More on next page)

Jaime:

- Born in South Africa. Lived there until age 4.

- Raised in Atlanta. Attended a small private high school.

- Came to UGA for the agricultural economics program.

- Has traveled to each continent

- Convinced their high school principal to use only locally grown foods in the cafeteria

- Plans to travel to Thailand this semester over break with their sister

- Does not own a car. Walks, bikes, or takes the bus everywhere.

- Volunteers at local Athens farms and helps them with their CSA program

- Participates in Susan G. Komen's Race for the Cure each year in memory of their grandmother

- One of seven children

- Was arrested in Italy last summer for speeding

Name:_____   Section:_____

2--Audience Analysis

Directions: For each of the following audiences, assess the opportunities and obstacles related to giving the particular kind of speech. Think, in particular, about how you might establish common ground and be audience-centered in your approach. You should also reflect on your own positionality in this process.

1. Audience: Undergraduate Science Majors
   Purpose: To Persuade
   Thesis: All science majors should be required to take a public speaking course.
Opportunities:

Obstacles:

2. Audience: Prospective Students' Parents or Guardians
   Purpose: To Inform
   Thesis: UGA requires students to live on campus in their first year.
Opportunities:

Obstacles:

3. Audience: UGA graduates and their friends and family
   Purpose: To Entertain
   Thesis: The UGA alumni community is the best in the nation.
Opportunities:

Obstacles:

3--Adapting to Your Audience

Directions: Imagine that a group of public speaking students have been asked to deliver a short speech to promote voter turnout among college students. Speakers are asked to use this opportunity to foster a positive spirit between campus Republicans and Democrats by emphasizing the importance of voting, no matter party affiliation. Answer the following questions before writing a short, one paragraph speech that could be delivered in this unique rhetorical context. Remember that your message should appeal to both Republicans and Democrats.

What do student Republicans and Democrats have in common? Write down at least six commonalities.

Identify the 2-3 themes above that you think would be most intriguing to this broad audience. Choose themes that go together, or could build logically off of one another, and write down what will become your main points.

Main point one:

Main point two:

Main point three:

Now, write a one-sentence thesis statement that captures the larger message articulated in your main points. The thesis statement should clearly and concisely express the message you want your audience to accept by the end of the speech.

_____

_____

Now that you've developed a thesis statement and main points, write a short speech that will foster a shared spirit of democracy for all students, no matter their party affiliation.

Name:_____   Section:_____

4--Speech Topic Audience Analysis

Directions: **Speaker**: Write your speech topic (subject) and purpose statement (how you are approaching it) below. Use as much detail as possible. You will then seek peer input. After you receive the completed survey, answer the questions found on the back of the next page. **Audience members**: Answers questions 1-5 and then provide some insight into your responses in the space below or in the margins. Please remember, the most helpful responses are honest and constructive.

Speech Topic:_____

Specific Purpose Statement:_____

----- ----- ----- ----- ----- ----- ----- ----- ----- ----- ----- ----- -----

1. Name:_____

1. Interest Level: (not at all) **1   2   3** (very interested!)
2. Knowledge Level: (I know nothing) **1   2   3** (I'm nearly an expert!)
3. How relevant is this topic to the audience? :   (not at all) **1   2   3** (completely!)
4. Is the specific purpose statement clear?   **YES   NO**
5. Is this topic narrow enough to fit into the time limit?   **YES   NO**

2. Name:_____

1. Interest Level: (not at all) **1   2   3** (very interested!)
2. Knowledge Level: (I know nothing) **1   2   3** (I'm nearly an expert!)
3. How relevant is this topic to the audience? :   (not at all) **1   2   3** (completely!)
4. Is the specific purpose statement clear?   **YES   NO**
5. Is this topic narrow enough to fit into the time limit?   **YES   NO**

3. Name:_____

1. Interest Level: (not at all) **1   2   3** (very interested!)
2. Knowledge Level: (I know nothing) **1   2   3** (I'm nearly an expert!)
3. How relevant is this topic to the audience? :   (not at all) **1   2   3** (completely!)
4. Is the specific purpose statement clear?   **YES   NO**
5. Is this topic narrow enough to fit into the time limit?   **YES   NO**

4. Name:_____

   1. Interest Level: (not at all) **1   2   3** (very interested!)

   2. Knowledge Level: (I know nothing) **1   2   3** (I'm nearly an expert!)

   3. How relevant is this topic to the audience? :   (not at all) **1   2   3** (completely!)

   4. Is the specific purpose statement clear?   **YES   NO**

   5. Is this topic narrow enough to fit into the time limit?   **YES   NO**

5. Name:_____

   1. Interest Level: (not at all) **1   2   3** (very interested!)

   2. Knowledge Level: (I know nothing) **1   2   3** (I'm nearly an expert!)

   3. How relevant is this topic to the audience? :   (not at all) **1   2   3** (completely!)

   4. Is the specific purpose statement clear?   **YES   NO**

   5. Is this topic narrow enough to fit into the time limit?   **YES   NO**

6. Name:_____

   1. Interest Level: (not at all) **1   2   3** (very interested!)

   2. Knowledge Level: (I know nothing) **1   2   3** (I'm nearly an expert!)

   3. How relevant is this topic to the audience? :   (not at all) **1   2   3** (completely!)

   4. Is the specific purpose statement clear?   **YES   NO**

   5. Is this topic narrow enough to fit into the time limit?   **YES   NO**

7. Name:_____

   1. Interest Level: (not at all) **1   2   3** (very interested!)

   2. Knowledge Level: (I know nothing) **1   2   3** (I'm nearly an expert!)

   3. How relevant is this topic to the audience? :   (not at all) **1   2   3** (completely!)

   4. Is the specific purpose statement clear?   **YES   NO**

   5. Is this topic narrow enough to fit into the time limit?   **YES   NO**

8. Name:_____

    1. Interest Level: (not at all) **1 2 3** (very interested!)

    2. Knowledge Level: (I know nothing) **1 2 3** (I'm nearly an expert!)

    3. How relevant is this topic to the audience? :   (not at all) **1 2 3** (completely!)

    4. Is the specific purpose statement clear?   **YES NO**

    5. Is this topic narrow enough to fit into the time limit?   **YES NO**

9. Name:_____

    1. Interest Level: (not at all) **1 2 3** (very interested!)

    2. Knowledge Level: (I know nothing) **1 2 3** (I'm nearly an expert!)

    3. How relevant is this topic to the audience? :   (not at all) **1 2 3** (completely!)

    4. Is the specific purpose statement clear?   **YES NO**

    5. Is this topic narrow enough to fit into the time limit?   **YES NO**

10. Name:_____

    1. Interest Level: (not at all) **1 2 3** (very interested!)

    2. Knowledge Level: (I know nothing) **1 2 3** (I'm nearly an expert!)

    3. How relevant is this topic to the audience? :   (not at all) **1 2 3** (completely!)

    4. Is the specific purpose statement clear?   **YES NO**

    5. Is this topic narrow enough to fit into the time limit?   **YES NO**

11. Name:_____

    1. Interest Level: (not at all) **1 2 3** (very interested!)

    2. Knowledge Level: (I know nothing) **1 2 3** (I'm nearly an expert!)

    3. How relevant is this topic to the audience? :   (not at all) **1 2 3** (completely!)

    4. Is the specific purpose statement clear?   **YES NO**

    5. Is this topic narrow enough to fit into the time limit?   **YES NO**

12. Name:_____

    1. Interest Level: (not at all) **1 2 3** (very interested!)

    2. Knowledge Level: (I know nothing) **1 2 3** (I'm nearly an expert!)

    3. How relevant is this topic to the audience? :   (not at all) **1 2 3** (completely!)

    4. Is the specific purpose statement clear?   **YES NO**

    5. Is this topic narrow enough to fit into the time limit?   **YES NO**

13. Name:_____

    1. Interest Level: (not at all) **1 2 3** (very interested!)

    2. Knowledge Level: (I know nothing) **1 2 3** (I'm nearly an expert!)

    3. How relevant is this topic to the audience? :   (not at all) **1 2 3** (completely!)

    4. Is the specific purpose statement clear?   **YES NO**

    5. Is this topic narrow enough to fit into the time limit?   **YES NO**

-----   -----   -----   -----   -----   -----   -----   -----   -----   -----   -----   -----   -----

Speaker: Review your survey results and then provide three different ways that your audience survey will influence your strategic plan for your upcoming speech.

    1.

    2.

    3.

5--Evidence Research

Directions: Find *at least three* sources for your next speech. You should submit a complete and correct bibliographic citation for each source. For each source you should describe the argument made by the author and explain how it will enhance your speech. You should also assess the credibility of the source material.

1.   **Source Citation**:

Describe what element from the S.U.P.P.O.R.T.S. table (see first section of the workbook) this source adds to your speech:

Please explain why you believe that the author(s) of the document should be considered a credible source on this particular issue:

2.   **Source Citation**:

Describe what element from the S.U.P.P.O.R.T.S. table (see first section of this workbook) this source adds to your speech:

Please explain why you believe that the author(s) of the document should be considered a 1) highly credible source, 2) somewhat credible source, 3) weak or uncertain source on this particular issue:

3. **Source Citation**:

Describe what element from the S.U.P.P.O.R.T.S. table (see first section of this workbook) this source adds to your speech:

Please explain why you believe that the author(s) of the document should be considered a 1) highly credible source, 2) somewhat credible source, 3) weak or uncertain source on this particular issue:

4. **Source Citation**:

Describe what element from the S.U.P.P.O.R.T.S. table (see first section of this workbook) this source adds to your speech:

Please explain why you believe that the author(s) of the document should be considered a credible source on this particular issue:

6--Testing Evidence

Directions: The previous exercise helped you to analyze evidence in the early stages of research. This exercise is meant to analyze your use of evidence once the speech is drafted. Read your own outline and answer the questions below. See below for a sample answer to question one.

"Yes. For point 1, I use a special report from the New York Times. For point 2, I provide statistics from the CDC. And for point 3, I provide expert testimony from my US American History professor."

1. Are all of the main points of the speech supported by some form of evidence?

2. Does the speech clearly identify the source of evidence? How is each source set-up in the speech?

3. Is the evidence from sources that are credible? Does the evidence avoid an institutional or personal bias?

4. Does the speech contain different kinds of evidence or S.U.P.P.O.R.T.S.?

5.   Is the evidence stated in specific terms that the audience will understand?

6.   Does the speech contain sufficient evidence to persuade/inform/entertain the audience?

7.   Does the speech contain evidence to address predictable objections that may be raised by the audience? How so?

8.   Does the speech contain evidence that the audience will consider new or interesting?

7--Researching Speech Topics

Directions: For each of the topics below, indicate which types of supporting material could be *effective* and which types would be *less* effective for the topic. Be prepared to justify your reasoning.

Supporting Material

Expert Testimony	Narrative	Definition	Fact
Statistic	Real Examples		Lay Testimony
Figurative Analogy	Witness Testimony	Literal Analogy	

Topic 1: The Best Coffee in Athens
Effective Support:

Less Effective Support:

Topic 2: Why I Came to UGA
Effective Support:

Less Effective Support:

Topic 3: The History of Baseball
    Effective Support:

    Less Effective Support:

Topic 4: The Best Apps for Food Delivery in Athens
    Effective Support:

    Less Effective Support:

Topic 5: Changing the UGA game day parking policy
    Effective Support:

    Less Effective Support:

8--Supporting Material

Directions: First, identify the argument (underline) and supporting material (star) for items 2-8. Then, determine the type of supporting material used (pgs. 142-146). Next, in full sentences, evaluate whether or not the speaker has used convincing support material and why. Finally, rewrite the supporting material to make it more appropriate for the argument. The new supporting evidence may be hypothetical.

1. EXAMPLE: <u>My plan to increase parking opportunities by building a "super-sized" parking deck on the edge of campus will work here at UGA.</u> *Athens Tech built a large parking structure on the edge of their campus three years ago to solve their parking problems and it has worked marvelously. The students, faculty, and staff no longer report parking as a major cause of stress.*

Type of supporting material: literal analogy

Supporting material evaluation and sentence re-write: *A literal analogy is only persuasive when the two things being compared are similar in the situation being discussed. While the two institutions are located in the same area, they are not similar in terms of campus and population size. Athens Tech's campus is much smaller and serves a smaller student body than UGA's campus. Therefore, the supporting material is a poor choice.*
*University of Florida, a school similar in size and environment to UGA, built a large parking structure on the edge of their campus to solve their parking problems and it has worked marvelously. The students, faculty, and staff no longer report parking as a major cause of stress. *

2. Bicycle accidents are a huge problem here at UGA. My roommate Bruce, my best friend Sarah, and my lab-partner Jordan have all told me that they have gotten in bicycle accidents.

3. Global warming affects us all in this classroom. I asked my environmental biology teacher, Dr. Samir Globi, about global warming's effects on us in Athens. He said that every day we inhale semi-toxic chemicals that should not be present in our air, but are because of global warming.

4. Athenians are incredibly courageous and resilient people. Over the course of hundreds of years, residents of this city have overcome many of obstacles in order to create a more just and welcoming community.

5. If we do not address the problem of littering on gamedays, it is only going to get worse. A ball in motion stays in motion unless it is acted upon by an external force. It is time we became that external force.

6. I know some of you might be thinking that my plan costs too much to be a feasible solution to our current homelessness problem here in Athens. But, let me try to convince you otherwise by providing you with three experts who believe that my plan is feasible. The current mayor of Athens and Condi Burnett, who runs the Athens Area Homelessness Coalition, have each gone on record to state that a plan that is very similar to mine is not only feasible, but cost-effective.

7. All UGA students are affected by UGA's current football ticket policy. According to *dictionary.com*, affected means "to be influenced in a harmful way," and therefore something must be done to change UGA's policy.

8. Stress is a leading contributor to illegal vaping on campus. In a survey done by the Health Center last year, they found that 75% of students report experiencing extreme stress at some point during each semester. A report done by the Office of Public Safety found that 60% of undergraduate engage in illegal vaping at some point in the semester. Clearly, stress is causing illegal vaping for undergraduate students.

9--Using Paradigms to Strengthen Arguments

Directions: In the *Rhetoric*, Aristotle writes that a speaker can convince an audience of a general principle by supporting it with a specific example, which he calls a *paradigm*. For Aristotle, paradigms can be historical events, comparative scenarios or animal fables invented for the occasion. This activity will give you practice assessing and inventing paradigms. A good paradigm seems to be convincing because it is vivid, pithy and memorable. It doesn't have to be logically valid, but it does have to seem persuasive and appropriate to the audience. Paradigms can complement other methods of support, including factual evidence.

This activity will give you practice in assessing paradigms and designing your own.

Here are three paradigms that support the same general principle. The first is historical, the second is a comparative scenario, and the third is an animal fable. For each one, consider what is convincing about it and what is unconvincing. When considering what is unconvincing, consult pages 151 to 152 about fallacies in the textbook. Then rewrite each paradigm so that it is stronger, preserving the same core elements of the original version.

1. *Taking two finals in one day is an impossible undertaking. My roommate took two finals in one day last semester, and he failed them both even though he studied hard.*

Convincing elements:

Unconvincing elements:

Revised version:

2. *Taking two finals in one day is an impossible undertaking. It's like driving two cars at the same time.*

Convincing elements:

Unconvincing elements:

Revised version:

3. *Taking two finals in one day is an impossible undertaking. When ants try to carry two crumbs at once, they drop them both.*

Convincing elements:

Unconvincing elements:

Revised version:

> Factual evidence can be complemented by an appropriate paradigm to make an argument stronger. Consider the following example: *You should wear sunblock that blocks ultraviolet rays whenever you go outside. The United States Department of Health and Human Services has determined that ultraviolet rays cause skin cancer. My uncle never wore sunblock, and he died of cancer.*
>
> For each of the three following general propositions, think of one piece of supporting factual evidence and one paradigm that can complement it.

1. For this proposition, think of a historical paradigm:

You should always read books on paper instead of on a tablet.

2. For this one, think of a comparative scenario paradigm:

When you host a dinner party, always provide your guests with a vegetarian option.

3. For this one, think of an animal fable:

Make sure to have at least $20 in your wallet at all times.

Now go back to the first three examples about taking two final exams in one day. For each example, think of one piece of factual evidence that could complement the original paradigms to make them more convincing. Write that evidence in the margins near the paradigms.

10--Flawed Introductions

Directions: Below you will find four flawed introductions to different types of speeches. First, identify the problems in each introduction. For instance, consider if each component in the introduction is present. Then, fix these introductions by re-writing sections, creating new sentences, or overhauling the entire introduction. Be sure to review Chapter 5 as you complete this assignment and consider concerns of ethos, pathos, and logos.

1. In my speech, I will argue that the Miller Learning Center does not adequately serve student needs. First, I will describe the needs a typical college student has every day. Then, I will discuss how the services the MLC provides does not meet these needs. And, finally, I will provide a plan that the MLC can adopt to better serve its student population.

2. Last week I did something that makes me cringe even thinking about it. And, it was not my first time doing this thing. In fact, I do this thing as often as I can. What am I talking about, you ask? Giving blood. Yes, even though I consider myself among the "needle averse" population, I still donate as much as I can and after listening to this speech, I hope you might be more interested in donating blood. However, my purpose here today is not to persuade you, but rather to inform you about blood donation. So, to start, I will explain why blood donations are even needed. Second, I will describe the blood donation process. And, third, I will explain what happens to the blood after it leaves the donor's body.

3. "I pledge allegiance to the flag of the United States of America," continue with me if you would like, "and to the Republic for which it stands. One nation. Under God. Indivisible. With liberty and justice for all." Not bad! Most of you likely did not have to think too hard to chime in because you have said those words thousands of times in school. However, some of you did not chime. Why? You did not know the words. Or maybe you knew the words but did not want to repeat them? If you find yourself in any of these groups, you are not alone. Today I am going to inform you all about the controversy over the pledge. While it might not be controversial to say the pledge in your hometown, it is becoming a national conversation and we should all be informed about it so we can make up our own minds.

4. It's the most wonderful time of the year. No, I am not talking about the winter holidays. Y'all probably know exactly what I am talking about: football season! If you are a football fan like me, you count down the hours until kick off every Saturday. This year, unfortunately, the excitement is accompanied by fear. Fear that I will get trampled or pass out waiting in line to gain admission to the game. Last year, the UGA Athletic Association adopted a new policy for student tickets that is ripe with flaws. I hope you will agree with me after you listen to my speech.

11--Introduction Draft Evaluation

Directions: First, craft an introduction for your speech. Remember, a strong introduction will *gain the audience's attention, state the purpose of the speech, establish your credibility, provide reasons to listen*, and *preview the main points*. Consider these as they relate to concerns of ethos, pathos, and logos as you craft your introduction. Then, swap your draft with a partner for evaluation. Partners should identify the components of an introduction in your draft (you can circle or underline and write in the margins for this part) and utilize terminology from Chapter 5 to identify any potential areas that could be improved.

Areas for Improvement:

12--Main Ideas

Directions: Imagine that each of the phrases below lists the main ideas contained in a single speech. Explain what is wrong with these main ideas and attempt to improve them (there might be multiple problems). Then, identify the organizational pattern your re-write would follow. Finally, write a preview statement for your introduction that contains your main points for your upcoming speech. You should also note your organizational pattern. Be sure to refer to Chapter 4, beginning with page 63, as you complete this activity.

1. The John Lewis Voting Act, John Lewis's early life, John Lewis's Civil Rights activism

    Problem(s):

    Re-write:

    Organizational Pattern:

2. A guitar strings' weight, a guitar body's wood type, the history of the guitar

    Problem(s):

    Re-write:

    Organizational Pattern:

3. Beaches in the Pacific Northwest, beaches in the Gulf Coast, why beaches are my favorite travel spot

    Problem(s):

    Re-write:

    Organizational Pattern:

4. Symbolism of the Olympic rings, symbolism of international sports, symbolism of the Olympic torch

    Problem(s):

    Re-write:

    Organizational Pattern:

5. The problem of contamination in recycling, recycling contamination is caused by limited recycling education, the solution for recycling contamination is increasing composting sites

    Problem(s):

    Re-write:

    Organizational Pattern:

6. The history of Athens, Georgia

    Problem(s):

    Re-write:

    Organizational Pattern:

7. My main points

    Preview Statement for Introduction:

    Organizational Pattern:

13—Full-Sentence Outline Peer Critique

Directions: Read your partner's full-sentence outline in its entirety. This should take you several minutes. While reading the outline, mark all spelling, grammatical, and typographical errors. After you have read the entire outline, answer the questions on this worksheet. Be specific and candid with your responses.

INTRODUCTION

1. Does your partner have the required pieces of the introduction? If not, identify the missing pieces on their outline.

2. Does the attention getter actually grab your attention? Provide an alternative attention getter.

3. Does your partner clearly reveal their topic?

4. Write a sentence that would tell the audience why the speech is relevant to their lives. Where might your partner insert this line?

5. How does your partner establish credibility? Are these statements compelling? Why or why not.

6. What are your partner's main points?

7. Is the thesis clear and concise? If not, write a thesis that more clearly reflects the main points.

BODY

1. What organizational pattern did your partner choose? Was this a good choice? Why or why not.

2. Are your partner's main points balanced? If not, which one receives too much attention or too little attention? How might your partner solve this problem?

3. Are the main points clear? What might make the main points clearer?

4. Has your partner employed transitions? What types have they used? Where might another transition be useful?

5. How many sources has your partner cited? Which source is most credible? Which is least credible? Why?

6. Does your partner provide set-up, execution, and analysis for each source?

CONCLUSION

1. Has your partner crafted a sentence that lets the audience know they are transitioning into the conclusion?

2. Has your partner summarized all main points? Does this statement reflect what was said in the introduction?

3. Does your partner have a line that signifies the completion of the speech? What might be an alternative way to signal the end?

OVERALL

1. Has your partner included a works cited or bibliography page? Does it seem to be in the correct format?

2. Does your partner have an adequate amount of information for the time limit? Do they have too much?

3. How is this topic challenging for a college student to address? Is it too simple?

4. Has your partner adapted their topic to our class/audience? Is it compelling and interesting? Identify two ways that your partner might make their speech more compelling.

14--Working Outline

Directions: Use the following blank outline to create a working outline of your upcoming speech. You may not need all of the sub-points or you might need more. Feel free to adapt to your needs, but be sure to maintain an ordered speech.

I. INTRODUCTION: The introduction must fulfil all five functions listed below. Feel free to re-organize the functions based on your needs.

    A. [Gain audience attention and interest]

    B. [State the purpose of your speech]

    C. [Provide reasons to listen]

    D. [Establish credibility]

    E. [Thesis and preview]

Transition to Main Idea 1:

II: [Topic Sentence]:

    A. [*Supporting point/material for Main Idea 1*]:

        1. [*Supporting point/material for point A, if necessary*]:

        2. [*Supporting point/material for point A, if necessary*]:

    B. [*Supporting point/material for Main Idea 1*]:

        1. [*Supporting point/material for sub-point B, if necessary*]:

        2. [*Supporting point/material for sub-point B, if necessary*]:

    C. [*Supporting point/material for Main Idea 1*]:

Transition to Main Idea 2:

III: [Topic Sentence]:

    A. [*Supporting point/material for Main Idea 2*]:

        1. [*Supporting point/material for point A, if necessary*]:

        2. [*Supporting point/material for point A, if necessary*]:

    B. [*Supporting point/material for Main Idea 2*]:

        1. [*Supporting point/material for sub-point B, if necessary*]:

        2. [*Supporting point/material for sub-point B, if necessary*]:

    C. [*Supporting point/material for Main Idea 2*]:

Transition to Main Idea 3:

IV: [Topic Sentence]:

    A. [*Supporting point/material for Main Idea 3*]:

        1. [*Supporting point/material for point A, if necessary*]:

        2. [*Supporting point/material for point A, if necessary*]:

    B. [*Supporting point/material for Main Idea 3*]:

        1. [*Supporting point/material for sub-point B, if necessary*]:

        2. [*Supporting point/material for sub-point B, if necessary*]:

    C. [*Supporting point/material for Main Idea 3*]:

Transition to Conclusion:

V. CONCLUSION

    A. [Restatement of Thesis]:

    B. [Review Main Points]:

    C. [Concluding Device]:

15--Language and Style

Directions: Improve each of the following lines from student's speeches using the rhetorical schemes and figures discussed in the textbook (pgs. 165-167). Make sure to only use a scheme or figure once to maximize your creativity.

1. Athens is such a great city.

2. When my phone rang, I was so scared.

3. Democracy is probably the most important idea in America.

4. Casey and Morgan are an awesome couple.

5. You wouldn't believe how beautiful the Taj Mahal is until you see it in person.

6. The parking problem at UGA is really bad.

7. Ode to UGA

    I like you.

    You've been good to me.

    You've given me many things.

    I've learned so much from you.

    I'll never forget you.

    Thanks a bunch, UGA.

16--Parsimony

Directions: Parsimony means being economical, even stingy, with your words. To maximize parsimony, speakers should:
*Eliminate words that aren't needed
*Not say what you can expect your audience to infer
*Not repeat without a purpose
In this exercise, rewrite the short and long examples to maximize parsimony.

Short Examples:

1. In my speech today I would like to tell you about something that is pretty special.

2. If we would just be willing to take a little bit more time when we have the time to do so then we would probably be likely to do a better job.

3. I am thinking that this will probably have a very strong effect.

Long Example:
Rewrite this paragraph in 35 words or less:

- o **Our team decided on building a rectangular truss bridge. Our two options were between an arched truss and a rectangle truss bridge. After comparing the two, the rectangular truss bridge came out on top. It was simply the most economically friendly as well as the sturdiest and most reliable of the two bridges. We built and tested the rectangular truss bridge. The regulations were adhered to and upon completion of our prototype online we tweaked the design and made corrections to any errors present in the design. (88 words)**

58

17--Free Speech, Decorum, and Ceremonial Speaking

Directions: Watch Senator Ben Sasse's Commencement Speech to Fremont High School (Nebraska) here: https://youtu.be/vyfHRlPrUds

Then, respond to the following questions in complete sentences.

1. In what ways does Sasse violate the conventions of commencement speeches?

2. Is this an instance of the acceptability of violating accepted norms of speaking? Why or why not?

3. What can we learn from examples like this? In other words, how and why is it helpful to you, as a public speaking student, to consider whether or not speakers should be held to shared norms of speaking in particular contexts?

4. Sasse clearly sees this as an opportunity to exercise his free speech and discuss some political matters. Others disagreed. What sort of issues does this speech raise with regard to the values of civility and democracy—values that are, at times, in direct conflict with one another?

5. Who was Sasse's audience? And does the answer to this question affect how we interpret whether this speech was "effective" or not?

6. Find other examples of speeches that violated accepted norms of decorum. Were these more effective? Why or why not?

18--"Toasting Public Speaking" Speech Activity

Directions: Select your topic from a combination of two things, one from each of the lists below and write a "toast" to that topic. The first list contains values we aspire to in the process of public speaking. The second list contains subjects from the textbook, lectures, and notes. In your Toast, combine a value with a subject in order to celebrate how the topic was helpful in teaching you to give speeches. The toast should last approximately 1-2 minutes, and should represent all the aspects of content, organization, language, and delivery that you have learned this semester. Be sure to draw on the conventions of epideictic speaking and stylistic language from Chapter 9.

List #1 (Values)
Connection
Well-developed
Respectful
Relatability
Creativity
Storytelling
Immediacy
Thoughtfulness
Deliberateness
Strategic
Efficiency
Intentionality

List #2 (Subjects)
Speech topics
Conducting research
Speech anxiety
Outlining speeches
Ethics in public speaking
Speech note cards
Persuasive speeches
Logos, Ethos and Pathos
Supporting Materials
Vocal Delivery
Organization of Main Points
Links and connectives
Language Devices
Reasoning Fallacies
Speech rehearsal
Informative speeches
Working in groups
Respecting the audience
Special occasion speech

19--Components of Speaking Activity

Directions: Your instructor will assign your group to one of the components of speaking listed below. With your group members, compose as many reasons as possible to argue for why your assigned component is most important. Then, prepare your case to present to the rest of the class. Take notes as other groups speak below.

Group Member Names and Topic:

_____

_____

1. **SPEAKER DELIVERY:**

2. **SPEAKER REHEARSAL:**

3. **LANGUAGE**:

4. **CONTENT (main points, supporting materials, etc.)**:

5. **SPEECH ORGANIZATION**:

20--Constructing a Counterargument

Directions: For the following activity, review each policy speech topic and pose a counterargument to that speech's claim. Then, explain how you would refute that counterargument if it were your speech. Respond in complete sentences.

1. *Problem: Global warming and its implications as an effect of human activity.*
Solution: To reduce CO2 emissions, the policy will allot a limit of CO2 emissions for each household.

Possible Counterargument to this Proposal:

Possible Refutation to Above Counterargument:

2. *Problem: High rates of uninsured citizens, high cost of healthcare, and needless loss of life with current healthcare system.*
Solution: Universal health coverage through a single-payer system.

Possible Counterargument to this Proposal:

Possible Refutation to Above Counterargument:

3. *Problem: Slow traffic on campus due to people dropping off friends while still in the road.*
Solution: Increased enforcement of traffic codes, including the issuing of tickets for offenders.

Possible Counterargument to this Proposal:

Possible Refutation to Above Counterargument:

4. *Problem: Unrealistic body expectations in media.*
Solution: Create an unaltered images law that bans the use of photoshop and other enhancers.

Possible Counterargument to this Proposal:

Possible Refutation to Above Counterargument:

21--Policy Introduction Draft

Directions: In this activity, you will craft an introduction for your policy speech based on the components below. When you finish these steps, practice aloud to ensure each one works *together* to introduce your speech.

Attention-Getter:
- This may be a surprising and/or relevant fact or brief story that will engage the audience in your overall topic.

Establish the Topic and Purpose of Your Speech:
- Remember for the policy speech, you will identify a problem that *needs* to be address and outline a practical solution. Explain what the problem is briefly, but emphasize the purpose of the speech is to suggest a practical solution to that problem.

Motivate Interest in Your Topic:
- Here, you should explicitly state why your audience should be concerned about solving this issue.

Establish Credibility:
- Why are you a credible person to speak to the audience on this topic? What kind of research have you conducted or relevant experience(s) do you have?

Thesis:
- This should be a precise statement that describes how you will address the problem. You should name the policy for which you are advocating explicitly, keeping in mind that your goal is for the audience to be persuaded to act in support of this policy in some way.

Preview:
- How can the audience expect the rest of your speech to flow? Explain the steps you will take in order to prove your thesis statement. How can you do this clearly but creatively?

22-- Delivering Verbal Citations

Directions: Read the instructions for how to verbally cite the sources that you use in your speech. Then, using this information, complete the activity on the next page.

<u>What is needed to deliver a verbal citation?</u>

1. **Set-up:** Frame the piece of evidence you are going to deliver. Things to consider for a verbal delivery:
   a. What type of source are you going to cite as evidence?
      i. Verbal framing might be different depending on the different type of source (i.e., interview with expert vs. newspaper article).
   b. When was this evidence made available?
      i. Consider how the time-sensitivity of your particular source. Was it released this year? Month? Week?
   c. Is additional information needed to give the audience an appropriate background for the evidence you are presenting?
      i. If you're referencing an expert, will people know them or the significance of their role?
      ii. How familiar is your audience with this source? Do we need to explain more about the source?
2. **Execution:** There are two different approaches to the execution of the evidence.
   a. Direct Quote:
      i. If you are going to use a quote, make sure that you notify the audience that you are quoting by stating, "quote" when you begin and "end quote" when you finish.
   b. Paraphrasing:
      i. When paraphrasing, you are still required to give a verbal citation and frame the author or source, but less specificity to the original language is required.
3. **Analysis:** When you are finished quoting or paraphrasing, it is important to provide the audience with the implications of the evidence.
   a. If you used a direct quote, you can translate this in your own language to explain its significance.
   b. You should also relate the evidence back to your claim in order to directly state how it contributes to the advancement of your argument.

<u>Verbal Citation Checklist:</u>
   ◊ Has the source type been identified? (i.e., newspaper article, testimony, journal publication etc.)
   ◊ Is the publisher mentioned? If it is a less known source, is the significance/credibility outlined?
   ◊ Was the date or time of release revealed?

Activity: Improving the Verbal Citations

First, read the claim the speaker is trying to advance. Next, identify the issue with the stated evidence. Then, using the additional citation information, re-write the statement to address the identified issue. Additional research may be necessary to find or resolve the issue(s).

1. Claim: Americans should take action to remove the Electoral College system and replace it with the popular vote.
    a. Stated Evidence: Only 38% of Americans say they would keep the Electoral College.

Brenan, Megan. "61% of Americans Support Abolishing Electoral College.." *Gallup*, 24 Sept. 2020. Web. https://news.gallup.com/poll/320744/americans-support-abolishing-electoral-college.aspx.

Explain the issue:

Re-write the stated evidence addressing the issue:

2. Claim: Plastic water bottles should be banned to promote environmental sustainability.
    a. Stated Evidence: According to Pacific Institute, "making bottles to meet America's demand for bottled water uses more than 17 million barrels of oil annually, enough to fuel 1.3 million cars for a year. And that's not even including the oil used for transportation."

"Bottled Water and Energy Fact Sheet." *Pacific Institute,* Feb. 2007. Web.
        <http://pacinst.org/publication/bottled-water-and-energy-a-fact-sheet/>.

Explain the issue:

Re-write the stated evidence addressing the issue:

3. Claim: Childhood obesity is threatening the future health and prosperity of our nation.
    a. Stated Evidence: "Childhood obesity affects every organ system in the body," tweeted Dr. Seema Kumar

Storace, Rebecca Sharim. "Experts Weigh in on Childhood Obesity." *ABC News.* ABC News
        Network, 13 Mar. 2013. Web.

Explain the issue:

Re-write the stated evidence addressing the issue:

Name:_____ Section:_____

23--Vocal Variety

Directions: Below are the Concluding Remarks at the 2017 State of the University Address, delivered by University of Georgia President Jere W. Morehead, on January 25, 2017. All of the punctuation and capitalization has been removed from the speech. Read the excerpt and make notes on this page to guide how you would add vocal variety to the speech. Also, note key words or phrases where delivery might change the meaning or interpretation of the speech.

let me return to the central question of today's address what will the next chapter look like in the great story of the university of georgia our next chapter will be defined by three priorities 1 increasing scholarship support for our students 2 further enhancing our learning environment and 3 solving the grand challenges of our time today I am asking our faculty our staff our students and our alumni and friends to unite around these priorities to help write this next chapter and magnify the impact of the university of georgia to a scale never before imagined and as we forge ahead we do so supported by our great tradition but untethered to it reaching beyond the status quo soaring toward greatness at the highest level guided by the belief that the university of georgia is essential to a strong state of georgia to a vibrant nation and to a better world thanks again for joining me this afternoon and for your unwavering commitment to excellence at the university of georgia I look forward to all that we will accomplish this year and in the years ahead thank you for your continued support

Sample Full-Sentence Outline

Below is a sample outline for an informative speech about the role of religion for African American culture. [This outline provided by Dr. Nicole Hurt.]

CAUTION: Do not use as a guide until you discuss outline preferences with your instructor.

INTRODUCTION

A. [*Attention grabber*] Imagine you are dirt. You are stepped on, underappreciated, and worthless in the eyes of the world. Now imagine you have the same attributes, but you are a person.

B. [*Reveal topic and relate to audience*] This is all but a common issue throughout the history of African American culture and is sometimes still apparent today. This culture often looked for guidance in their religious beliefs and still does so today.

C. [*Establish credibility*] Being a religious person myself, its role in society throughout history is important information for me to acquire.
   1. With current events today, religion is all but disregarded, from its hypocrisy to its necessity.
   2. Through further research, the role of religion has been a significant one for multiple reasons, which we will discuss today.

D. [*Thesis and preview*] I intend on informing you of the role religion has played for the African American Culture during the Civil War, Civil Rights Movement, as well as its importance in today's society.

[*Transition*] Let's begin by discussing the role of religion during the Civil War for the African American society.

BODY

I. [*Main Point 1*] The Civil War was a period of separation, discrimination, and a fight for equality among society, and each territory believed God was on their side.
   A. It is obvious that slaves looked to religious ideals in order to find comfort.
      1. Associate Professor of Religious Studies, **Laurie Maffly-Kipp**, discusses that after emancipation, religious committees were organized to transition from property to citizens.
      2. Slaves that became middle class citizens also sought to build a religious life much like their white counterparts.
   B. Soldiers during the Civil War also sought religious comfort.
      1. The Southern Christian Leaders organization provided soldiers with bibles and other religious tracts.
      2. This led to what is commonly known as the Great Revival, where "approximately ten percent of the men engaged" accepted Christ, and there was constant worship, prayer, even baptism for the soldiers, according to historian and professor **Gordon Leidner**.
   C. Abolitionists were a key component, in the Civil War to gain slaves' rights, but it is not a well-known fact that abolitionists were actually the minority in society.

1. Those who opposed felt their actions were faulty since the Bible did not condemn slavery, as long as they were treated humanely and their souls were cared for.
2. Abolitionists still continued to publicly broadcast their stance, publishing articles as well as supporting legislation to ensure equality in justice.

[*Transition*] Overall, the Civil War fought against racial injustice, but did it succeed? If it had, some will argue the Civil Rights Movement would not have occurred, which we will discuss next.

II.   [*Main Point 2*] The Civil Rights Movement was more personal than slavery, for it discriminated against minority equal counterparts.
   A. White supremacy was a major catalyst in this era.
        1. Most viewed civil injustice as nothing more than the southern way of life.
   B. An important figure in white supremacy was the Ku Klux Klan.
        1. The KKK was a Christian ethnocentric group that terrorized supporters of the Civil Rights Movement, mostly minorities.
        2. Researcher **Michael Fisher** found that people viewed them as "brave white heroes who gallantly saved whites from aggressive blacks in the early 20th century."
        3. They manipulated the Bible as evidence that their actions were solely God's will.
   C. These types of threats against the African American culture created many popular religious organizations, such as the SCLC and SNCC.
        1. **Judith Rosenbaum**, a writer, educator, and historian, states "the [black] church served as the center of the Civil Rights Movement" in that it was the symbol of the movement, being the epitome of freedom, acceptance, love, and equality.
        2. It was also a meeting place for these religious organizations, leading to popular protests we read about in the history books today.
   D. These organizations would not have been formed without influential religious leaders.
        1. Martin Luther King Jr., a prominent figure at the March on Washington, along with 100 other ministers, founded the Southern Christian Leadership Conference and planned many nonviolent protests.
        2. Malcolm X is not a major prominent figure, but his is important from a religious perspective.
        3. While he worked with MLK Jr.'s plans, he is better known for his alternative solution- stop turning the other cheek.
        4. He stated, "Justice is not necessitated by love. We do not treat people justly because we like them or are partial to them. If that were the case there would be no need to command justice, since people are naturally just to those they favor. We need to be commanded with justice when dealing with those we have no favorable feelings toward."

[*Transition*] Now that we have seen the role of religion in the past, let's look at its impact on today's society.

III.   [*Main Point 3*] The black church is apparent in today's society in the media in multiple ways.
   A. Religion is a controversial topic today, and many view the church as hypocritical.

1. People believe in equality and justice, which have been passed into law, yet those who enacted the law do not practice it, and there are still obvious strains between races.
2. Ferguson, Missouri recently experienced racial tension as a minority was shot by a police officer, and racial injustice was a possible motive.
3. Pastor Ira Acree is one that is deciding to stand up for racial inequality in a way he thinks is religious.
   a) **Gregory Pratt** and **Kim Geiger**, local reporters of this event, received a statement from the pastor when he stated, "We will fight back. Not with violence, but with our voice. With discipline, with dignity, and with restraint."

CONCLUSION

A. [*Signal End and Review Thesis*] Today we have evaluated religion's role for the African American culture throughout history.
1. The Civil War used religion to provide soldiers and slaves with a hope of a near end of a war and injustice.
2. The Civil Rights Movement continued this fight against inequality by using the Church as the backbone of ethnocentric wrongdoing against minorities with nonviolent approaches to stand up for their beliefs.
3. Today, we still deal with racial injustice, but the church has provided those fighting with the confidence to stand up against others and fight for what they believe is right.
B. [*Concluding Device*] The African American culture survived through all of these trials with their belief that God would guide them to a future better life, and they still hold onto these values today. Without religion, we would have never been given the ability to create such historical organizations and eventually make history itself.

References

Abzug, Robert. "Abolition and Religion." *The Gilder Lehrman Institute of American History*. The Gilder Lehrman Institute of American History, n.d. Web. 19 Oct. 2014.

Fisher, Michael. "The Ku Klux Klan." *The Ku Klux Klan*. N.p., n.d. Web. 19 Oct. 2014.

Leidner, Gordon. "Religious Revival in Civil War Armies." *Great American History Civil War Religious Revivals*. Great American History, n.d. Web. 19 Oct. 2014.

Maffly-Kipp, Laurie F. "The Church in the Southern Black Community: Introduction." *The Church in the Southern Black Community: Introduction*. The University of North Caroline at Chapel Hill, May 2001. Web. 19 Oct. 2014.

Menzie, Nicola. "Christian Responses to #Ferguson Focus on Fear, Injustice and White Privilege." *Christian Post*. The Christian Post, 19 Aug. 2014. Web. 20 Oct. 2014.

Pratt, Gregory, and Kim Geiger. "Religious Leaders Call for Peaceful Activism in Wake of Trayvon Martin Case." *Chicago Tribune*. Chicago Tribune, 14 July 2013. Web. 20 Oct. 2014.

Rosenbaum, Judith. "Sharing Stories, Inspiring Change." *Clergy in the Civil Rights Movement: Introductory Essay*. Jewish Women's Archive, n.d. Web. 20 Oct. 2014.

Stout, Henry S. "Religion in the Civil War: The Southern Perspective, Divining America, TeacherServe, National Humanities Center." *Religion in the Civil War: The Southern Perspective, Divining America, TeacherServe, National Humanities Center*. TeacherServe, n.d. Web. 17 Oct. 2014.

Taylor, Clarence. "African American Religious Leadership and the Civil Rights Movement." *The Gilder Lehrman Institute of American History*. The Gilder Lehrman Institute of American History, n.d. Web. 19 Oct. 2014.

"The Role of Religion in the Civil Rights Movements." *Center for American Progress*. Center for American Progress, 9 June 2004. Web. 20 Oct. 2014.

Name:_____   *Section:*_____

Personal Report of Public Speaking Anxiety

Directions: Below are 34 statements that people sometimes make about themselves. Please indicate whether or not you believe each statement applies to you by marking whether you:

Strongly Disagree = 1; Disagree = 2; Neutral = 3; Agree = 4; Strongly Agree = 5.

_____1. While preparing for giving a speech, I feel tense and nervous.

_____2. I feel tense when I see the words "speech" and "public speech" on a course outline when studying.

_____3. My thoughts become confused and jumbled when I am giving a speech.

_____4. Right after giving a speech I feel that I have had a pleasant experience.

_____5. I get anxious when I think about a speech coming up.

_____6. I have no fear of giving a speech.

_____7. Although I am nervous just before starting a speech, I soon settle down after starting and feel calm and comfortable.

_____8. I look forward to giving a speech.

_____9. When the instructor announces a speaking assignment in class, I can feel myself getting tense.

_____10. My hands tremble when I am giving a speech.

_____11. I feel relaxed while giving a speech.

_____12. I enjoy preparing for a speech.

_____13. I am in constant fear of forgetting what I prepared to say.

_____14. I get anxious if someone asks me something about my topic that I don't know.

_____15. I face the prospect of giving a speech with confidence.

_____16. I feel that I am in complete possession of myself while giving a speech.

Source: James C. McCroskey, "Measures of communication-bound anxiety," *Speech Monographs* 37, no. 4 (1970): 269-277, last accessed July 8, 2021, http://www.jamescmccroskey.com/measures/prpsa.htm

_____17. My mind is clear when giving a speech.

_____18. I do not dread giving a speech.

_____19. I perspire just before starting a speech.

_____20. My heart beats very fast just as I start a speech.

_____21. I experience considerable anxiety while sitting in the room just before my speech starts.

_____22. Certain parts of my body feel very tense and rigid while giving a speech.

_____23. Realizing that only a little time remains in a speech makes me very tense and anxious.

_____24. While giving a speech, I know I can control my feelings of tension and stress.

_____25. I breathe faster just before starting a speech.

_____26. I feel comfortable and relaxed in the hour or so just before giving a speech.

_____27. I do poorer on speeches because I am anxious.

_____28. I feel anxious when the teacher announces the date of a speaking assignment.

_____29. When I make a mistake while giving a speech, I find it hard to concentrate on the parts that follow.

_____30. During an important speech I experience a feeling of helplessness building up inside me.

_____31. I have trouble falling asleep the night before a speech.

_____32. My heart beats very fast while I present a speech.

_____33. I feel anxious while waiting to give my speech.

_____34. While giving a speech, I get so nervous I forget facts I really know.

*Name:*_____ *Section:*_____

Peer Evaluation: Holistic

Directions: Take notes about your classmate's content and delivery on a separate sheet of paper during their speech. Then, use the following prompts to assess the speech and provide feedback for improvement. When possible, provide specific examples to support your observations. Be thorough and respond in complete sentences.

*Speaker's Name:*_____

*Speaker's Topic:*_____ *Date:*_____

1. What were the content (introduction, argument, language choices, organization, research, citations, evidence, examples, conclusion, etc.) strengths of your classmate's speech? Describe 2-3 strengths.

2. How might the speaker have improved the content of the speech? Provide 2-3 suggestions.

3. What were your classmate's delivery (facial expressions, eye contact, projection, inflection, enthusiasm, gestures, etc.) strengths?

4. How might the speaker have improved their delivery?

5. What should the speaker do to ensure that their next speech is even better than this one? Provide 3-4 specific suggestions.

*Name:*_____ *Section:*_____

Peer Evaluation: Holistic

Directions: Take notes about your classmate's content and delivery on a separate sheet of paper during their speech. Then, use the following prompts to assess the speech and provide feedback for improvement. When possible, provide specific examples to support your observations. Be thorough and respond in complete sentences.

*Speaker's Name:*_____

*Speaker's Topic:*_____ *Date:*_____

1. What were the content (introduction, argument, language choices, organization, research, citations, evidence, examples, conclusion, etc.) strengths of your classmate's speech? Describe 2-3 strengths.

2. How might the speaker have improved the content of the speech? Provide 2-3 suggestions.

3. What were your classmate's delivery (facial expressions, eye contact, projection, inflection, enthusiasm, gestures, etc.) strengths?

4. How might the speaker have improved their delivery?

5. What should the speaker do to ensure that their next speech is even better than this one? Provide 3-4 specific suggestions.

Peer Evaluation: Holistic

Directions: Take notes about your classmate's content and delivery on a separate sheet of paper during their speech. Then, use the following prompts to assess the speech and provide feedback for improvement. When possible, provide specific examples to support your observations. Be thorough and respond in complete sentences.

*Speaker's Name:*_____

*Speaker's Topic:*_____*Date:*_____

1. What were the content (introduction, argument, language choices, organization, research, citations, evidence, examples, conclusion, etc.) strengths of your classmate's speech? Describe 2-3 strengths.

2. How might the speaker have improved the content of the speech? Provide 2-3 suggestions.

3. What were your classmate's delivery (facial expressions, eye contact, projection, inflection, enthusiasm, gestures, etc.) strengths?

4. How might the speaker have improved their delivery?

5. What should the speaker do to ensure that their next speech is even better than this one? Provide 3-4 specific suggestions.

Peer Evaluation: Holistic

Directions: Take notes about your classmate's content and delivery on a separate sheet of paper during their speech. Then, use the following prompts to assess the speech and provide feedback for improvement. When possible, provide specific examples to support your observations. Be thorough and respond in complete sentences.

*Speaker's Name:*_____

*Speaker's Topic:*_____ *Date:*_____

1. What were the content (introduction, argument, language choices, organization, research, citations, evidence, examples, conclusion, etc.) strengths of your classmate's speech? Describe 2-3 strengths.

2. How might the speaker have improved the content of the speech? Provide 2-3 suggestions.

3. What were your classmate's delivery (facial expressions, eye contact, projection, inflection, enthusiasm, gestures, etc.) strengths?

4. How might the speaker have improved their delivery?

5. What should the speaker do to ensure that their next speech is even better than this one? Provide 3-4 specific suggestions.

Name:_____   Section:_____

Peer Evaluation: Delivery

Directions: Review the delivery chapter prior to completing this worksheet. the speech, evaluate your classmate's delivery using the form below. Provide 3-5 narrative comments below, indicating areas of clear strength or weakness.

Speaker's Name:_____

Speaker's Topic:_____Date:_____

KEY: **E**-excellent	**G**-good	**A**-average	**P**-poor	**N**-absent

Style

Conversational   E   G   A   P   N

Use of notecards   E   G   A   P   N

Eye Contact

Sustained/meaningful   E   G   A   P   N

Varied (made around the room)   E   G   A   P   N

Vocalics

Volume   E   G   A   P   N

Rate   E   G   A   P   N

Pitch   E   G   A   P   N

Pauses   E   G   A   P   N

Vocal variety   E   G   A   P   N

Pronunciation   E   G   A   P   N

Articulation   E   G   A   P   N

Physical manipulation:

Posture   E   G   A   P   N

Body movement   E   G   A   P   N

Facial expressions   E   G   A   P   N

Dress   E   G   A   P   N

Self-presentation/Poise   E   G   A   P   N

Notes/Comments:

*Name:*_____   *Section:*_____

Peer Evaluation: Supporting Materials

*Speaker's Name:*_____

*Speaker's Topic:*_____*Date:*_____

Part 1: Write down information about as many supporting materials that the speaker used as you can. Specifically, identify the source (e.g., publication title and/or author), date, and the essential content of material cited (i.e., what testimony, facts, statistics, analogies are presented as support).

1. Source	Content of Support Material	Date
2. Source	Content of Support Material	Date
3. Source	Content of Support Material	Date
4. Source	Content of Support Material	Date
5. Source	Content of Support Material	Date

Part 2: *Respond to the following questions concerning your peer's use of support.* <u>Respond in complete sentences.</u>

1. What main idea in your peer's speech was best supported by evidence? Explain your reasoning.

2. What main idea in your peer's speech was least well supported? If she or he were to give the speech again, what evidence would be necessary to fully support this idea? Explain your reasoning.

3. On a scale of 1–10 (1=incredibly difficult, 10=incredibly easy), how easy or difficult was it for you to discern *when* your peer was relying on support material? In other words, how well did the speaker clearly and consistently credit his or her sources verbally? Explain your reasoning.

4. Assess the quality of support materials cited in your peer's speech according to the criteria of *accuracy*, *authority*, *currency*, and *objectivity*. What source(s) are of questionable quality and what source(s) are of superb quality? Explain your reasoning.

Peer Evaluation: Language

Directions: During the speech, listen to your classmate's language choices. Jot down *at least 5 examples* of language choices that stand out due to appropriateness (for the speaker, audience, context, and topic), vividness (imagery, rhythm), inclusivity, familiarity, clarity, economy, power, variety *or lack thereof.* Then, complete the flip-side.

Speaker's
Name:_____

Speaker's Topic:_____Date:_____

1.

2.

3.

4.

5.

6.

7.

8.

9.

10.

1. What did the speaker do particularly *well* in terms of language choices (appropriateness (for the speaker, for the audience, for the context, for the topic), vividness (imagery, rhythm), inclusivity, familiarity, clarity, economy, power, variety)?

2. What does the speaker need to *work on* in terms of language for future speeches? Provide at least two ways to improve language.

3. Why do we study language in a public speaking class? Use *specific examples* from your classmate's speech to support your argument(s).